The Physical Education Teacher's Lesson Planner

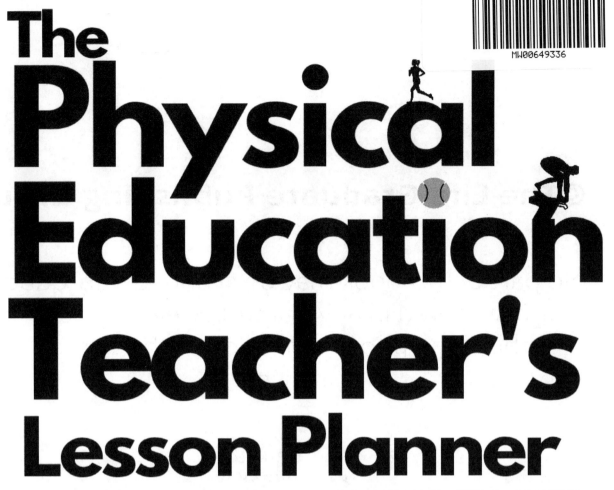

FOR THE ORGANIZED SPORTS TEACHER

ENDORSED BY

THE CREATOR OF

80 AWESOME SPORTS GAMES

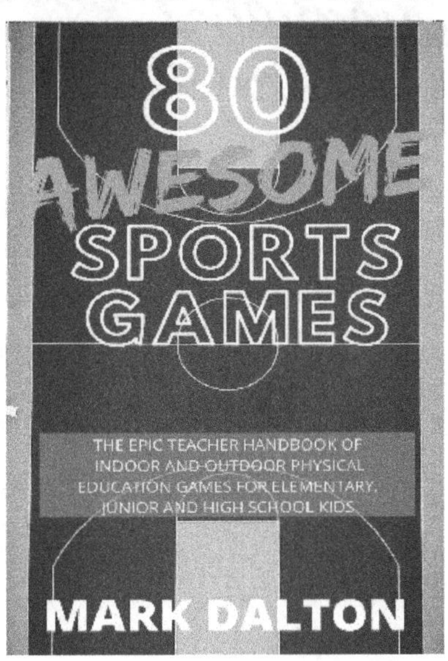

Education Planning
Series

The Basics of Planning Your P.E/Sport Lessons

Planning your Physical Education lessons is an important role of the P.E teacher given the unique challenges of the Physical Education teacher. Many P.E teachers perform a variety of roles such as the Homeroom Teacher, Classroom Teacher, Sports Coach, School Sport Coordinator, Health Teacher, Pastoral Care Coordinator along with many other responsibilities. There are not many positions at schools that require such a diverse range of skills than the Physical Education teacher and therefore planning and organization is imperative.

The Physical Education Teacher's Lesson Planner has been designed to help teachers to remain organized in advance of the lessons ahead. Yes, things on a daily basis can change but preparing as well as you can will help keep your students engaged and keep you free from being caught out planning lessons at the last minute.

At the beginning of the planner, you are provided with the opportunity to include important dates and events such as sporting carnivals, regional network meetings, school holidays and other important events that can be included to remain organized.

There will never be a 'one size fits all' lesson planner for teachers however, this planner has been designed specifically for the Physical Education Teacher in mind with the diverse range of lessons and activities that need to be planned on a weekly basis.

The Physical Education Teacher!

BONUS SECTION

CHECK OUT THE BACK PAGES OF THE PLANNER FOR HINTS ON

'PHYSICAL EDUCATION - GAME PLAY FUNDAMENTALS'

The Physical Education Teacher's Lesson Planner

The Physical Education Teacher's Lesson Planner

Name ....

School ....

Year ....

Your Position/Role ....

My Physical Education

Lesson Timetable

Print and stick your timetable below

My Physical Education

Lesson Timetable

Print and stick your timetable below

IMPORTANT CONTACTS

Name	Phone	Email

Venues

PROFESSIONAL DEVELOPMENT

List any Professional Development that you have organized or participate in during the school year

Date: **Total Hours of PD:**

Location:

Date: **Total Hours of PD:**

Location:

Date: **Total Hours of PD:**

Location:

Date: **Total Hours of PD:**

Location:

Overall Total Hours:

IMPORTANT SCHOOL DATES

Major School Events, Sporting Carnivals, School Term Holidays etc.

MONTH:

MONTH:

MONTH:

IMPORTANT SCHOOL DATES 

Major School Events, Sporting Carnivals, School Term Holidays etc.

MONTH:

MONTH:

MONTH:

IMPORTANT SCHOOL DATES 

Major School Events, Sporting Carnivals, School Term Holidays etc.

MONTH:

MONTH:

MONTH:

IMPORTANT SCHOOL DATES

Major School Events, Sporting Carnivals, School Term Holidays etc.

MONTH:

MONTH:

MONTH:

Week Commencing 23 / 8 /2023

Example

Planning Overview

Planning out your lessons in advance will provide Physical Education Teachers with the opportunity to deliver engaging and enjoyable classes for their students.

DAY	LESSON 1 *Details of Lesson*	LESSON 2 *Details of Lesson*	LESSON 3 *Details of Lesson*
MON	Year 8W - Gymnastics Unit Lesson Double of Periods 1 & 2 10 Mins - Warm-up & Stretching Split into 2 groups Group 1 - Pommel Horse Group 2 - Beam	Yr 8W Gymnastics Unit Lesson Double continues Swap groups around Group 1 - Beam Group 2 - Pommel Horse 15 mins near end - Gym Tag Final 5 mins - Group pack-up	Free Period - Planning for upcoming Cross Country
TUES	Free Period - Get computer system for X-Country Event arranged with Phil in I.T	Year 4E - Tennis Unit First 10 minutes: Warm-up Tag game (Tail tag) Body of Session: Serving Final 10 Minutes: Serving Comp.	Year 9B - Basketball Unit First 15 minutes: Warm-up game of Lazer Tag + stretching. Split into 3 rotating teams (round robin event). Resting team provide the umpires on rotation
WED	Free Period - Meeting with P.E & Health Dept. Planning for next Term	Year 6B - X- Country training First 10 minutes: Warm-up & stretching Quick Game of 'Boot ball' for 15 mins. Time all students are record results on class tracker	Year 9L - Basketball Unit First 15 minutes: Warm-up game of Lazer Tag + stretching. Split into 3 rotating teams (round robin event). Resting team provide the umpires on rotation
THURS	Year 4Q - Tennis Unit First 10 minutes: Warm-up Tag game (Tail tag) Body of Session: Serving Final 10 Minutes: Serving Comp.	Double Lesson Lessons 2 & 3 Bike Education Unit - All Year 7 students First 30 mins: Bike safety Video	Bike Education Unit - All Year 7's
FRI	Meeting with Heads of Department of Senior School to review teacher report writing and assesment	Senior School Meeting	Year 6D/C - X- Country training First 10 minutes: Warm-up & stretching Quick Game of 'Boot ball' for 15 mins. Time all students are record results on class tracker

Events, Coaching, After School Sport Commitments etc for the week

1. Network Regional Meeting on Tuesday at 1pm - St Mary's College, Brayer Street.
2. Basketball training at 4.30pm Thursday this week - School gym
3. Get onto Phil in I.T re: Cross Country software to determine times and placing for event
4. Senior School meeting on Friday A.M

Example

Planning Overview

Planning out your lessons in advance will provide Physical Education Teachers with the opportunity to deliver engaging and enjoyable classes for their students.

LESSON 4 *Details of Lesson*	**LESSON 5** *Details of Lesson*	**LESSON 6** *Details of Lesson*	*Additional class/info*
Year 6B – X- Country training First 10 minutes: Warm-up & stretching Jog the students around the X-country course so they become familiar for the event in 3 weeks time	Year 6F – X- Country training First 10 minutes: Warm-up & stretching Jog the students around the X-country course so they become familiar for the event in 3 weeks time	Year 4H – Tennis Unit First 10 minutes: Warm-up Tag game (Tail tag) Body of Session: Serving Final 10 Minutes: Serving Comp.	
Year 9P – Basketball Unit First 15 minutes: Warm-up game of Lazer Tag + stretching. Split into 3 rotating teams (round robin event). Resting team provide the umpires on rotation	Out of school: Regional Network Meeting	Out of school: Regional Network Meeting	Reminder to my Basketball Team to bring own basketball for training on Thursday.
Year 9L – Basketball Unit First 15 minutes: Warm-up game of Lazer Tag + stretching. Split into 3 rotating teams like yesterdays lesson with 9P	Year 8K – Gymnastics Unit Lesson Double of Periods 1 & 2 10 Mins – Warm-up & Stretching Split into 2 groups Group 1 – Pommel Horse Group 2 – Beam	Yr 8W Gymnastics Unit Lesson Double continues Swap groups around Group 1 – Beam Group 2 – Pommel Horse 15 mins near end – Gym Tag Final 5 mins – Group pack-up	
Year 9P – Health Lesson Double of Periods 4 & 5 First Session Video: Cardiovascular Disease	Year 9P – Health Cardiovascular Disease Cont.. Intro to new project: Run through the req: and what is expected for the project. Reminder: print off info to show class re: Dangers of smoking	Meeting with Clinton Peake to work out P.E Budget for next term	Basketball Coaching 4:30 this arvo.
Meeting with Lincoln Thomson re: Softball Coaching for next season	Year 9L – Health Lesson Double of Periods 4 & 5 First Session Video: Cardiovascular Disease	Year 9L – Health Cardiovascular Disease Cont.. Intro to new project: Run through like 9P lesson yesterday	

SATURDAY	**SUNDAY**
Basketball Coaching – Hilltop Arena at 9.15am	Playing golf – 7.45am T-Off.

Week Commencing / /

DAY	LESSON 1 *Details of Lesson*	LESSON 2 *Details of Lesson*	LESSON 3 *Details of Lesson*	LESSON 4 *Details of Lesson*
MON				
TUES				
WED				
THURS				
FRI				

Events, Coaching, After School Sport Commitments etc for the week

LESSON 5 *Details of Lesson*	LESSON 6 *Details of Lesson*	LESSON 7 *Details of Lesson*	LESSON 8 *Details of Lesson*

SATURDAY	SUNDAY

Week Commencing / /

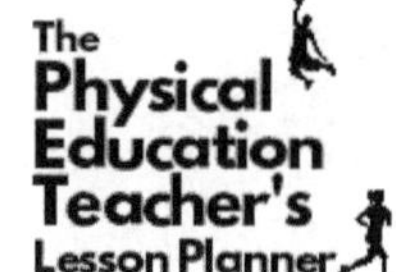

DAY	LESSON 1 Details of Lesson	LESSON 2 Details of Lesson	LESSON 3 Details of Lesson	LESSON 4 Details of Lesson
MON				
TUES				
WED				
THURS				
FRI				

Events, Coaching, After School Sport Commitments etc for the week

LESSON 5 *Details of Lesson*	**LESSON 6** *Details of Lesson*	**LESSON 7** *Details of Lesson*	**LESSON 8** *Details of Lesson*

SATURDAY	**SUNDAY**

Week Commencing / /

DAY	LESSON 1 Details of Lesson	LESSON 2 Details of Lesson	LESSON 3 Details of Lesson	LESSON 4 Details of Lesson
MON				
TUES				
WED				
THURS				
FRI				

Events, Coaching, After School Sport Commitments etc for the week

LESSON 5 *Details of Lesson*	LESSON 6 *Details of Lesson*	LESSON 7 *Details of Lesson*	LESSON 8 *Details of Lesson*

SATURDAY	SUNDAY

Week Commencing / /

DAY	LESSON 1 *Details of Lesson*	LESSON 2 *Details of Lesson*	LESSON 3 *Details of Lesson*	LESSON 4 *Details of Lesson*
MON				
TUES				
WED				
THURS				
FRI				

Events, Coaching, After School Sport Commitments etc for the week

LESSON 5 *Details of Lesson*	LESSON 6 *Details of Lesson*	LESSON 7 *Details of Lesson*	LESSON 8 *Details of Lesson*

SATURDAY	SUNDAY

Week Commencing / /

DAY	LESSON 1 *Details of Lesson*	LESSON 2 *Details of Lesson*	LESSON 3 *Details of Lesson*	LESSON 4 *Details of Lesson*
MON				
TUES				
WED				
THURS				
FRI				

Events, Coaching, After School Sport Commitments etc for the week

LESSON 5 *Details of Lesson*	LESSON 6 *Details of Lesson*	LESSON 7 *Details of Lesson*	LESSON 8 *Details of Lesson*

SATURDAY	SUNDAY

Week Commencing / /

DAY	LESSON 1 *Details of Lesson*	LESSON 2 *Details of Lesson*	LESSON 3 *Details of Lesson*	LESSON 4 *Details of Lesson*
MON				
TUES				
WED				
THURS				
FRI				

Events, Coaching, After School Sport Commitments etc for the week

LESSON 5 *Details of Lesson*	LESSON 6 *Details of Lesson*	LESSON 7 *Details of Lesson*	LESSON 8 *Details of Lesson*

SATURDAY	SUNDAY

Week Commencing / /

DAY	LESSON 1 Details of Lesson	LESSON 2 Details of Lesson	LESSON 3 Details of Lesson	LESSON 4 Details of Lesson
MON				
TUES				
WED				
THURS				
FRI				

Events, Coaching, After School Sport Commitments etc for the week

LESSON 5 *Details of Lesson*	LESSON 6 *Details of Lesson*	LESSON 7 *Details of Lesson*	LESSON 8 *Details of Lesson*

SATURDAY	SUNDAY

Week Commencing 

DAY	LESSON 1 *Details of Lesson*	LESSON 2 *Details of Lesson*	LESSON 3 *Details of Lesson*	LESSON 4 *Details of Lesson*
MON				
TUES				
WED				
THURS				
FRI				

Events, Coaching, After School Sport Commitments etc for the week

LESSON 5 *Details of Lesson*	LESSON 6 *Details of Lesson*	LESSON 7 *Details of Lesson*	LESSON 8 *Details of Lesson*

SATURDAY	SUNDAY

Week Commencing / /

DAY	LESSON 1 *Details of Lesson*	LESSON 2 *Details of Lesson*	LESSON 3 *Details of Lesson*	LESSON 4 *Details of Lesson*
MON				
TUES				
WED				
THURS				
FRI				

Events, Coaching, After School Sport Commitments etc for the week

LESSON 5 *Details of Lesson*	LESSON 6 *Details of Lesson*	LESSON 7 *Details of Lesson*	LESSON 8 *Details of Lesson*

SATURDAY	SUNDAY

Week Commencing / /

DAY	LESSON 1 *Details of Lesson*	LESSON 2 *Details of Lesson*	LESSON 3 *Details of Lesson*	LESSON 4 *Details of Lesson*
MON				
TUES				
WED				
THURS				
FRI				

Events, Coaching, After School Sport Commitments etc for the week

LESSON 5 *Details of Lesson*	LESSON 6 *Details of Lesson*	LESSON 7 *Details of Lesson*	LESSON 8 *Details of Lesson*

SATURDAY	SUNDAY

Week Commencing / /

DAY	LESSON 1 *Details of Lesson*	LESSON 2 *Details of Lesson*	LESSON 3 *Details of Lesson*	LESSON 4 *Details of Lesson*
MON				
TUES				
WED				
THURS				
FRI				

Events, Coaching, After School Sport Commitments etc for the week

LESSON 5 *Details of Lesson*	LESSON 6 *Details of Lesson*	LESSON 7 *Details of Lesson*	LESSON 8 *Details of Lesson*

SATURDAY	SUNDAY

Week Commencing / /

DAY	LESSON 1 Details of Lesson	LESSON 2 Details of Lesson	LESSON 3 Details of Lesson	LESSON 4 Details of Lesson
MON				
TUES				
WED				
THURS				
FRI				

Events, Coaching, After School Sport Commitments etc for the week

LESSON 5 *Details of Lesson*	LESSON 6 *Details of Lesson*	LESSON 7 *Details of Lesson*	LESSON 8 *Details of Lesson*

SATURDAY	SUNDAY

Week Commencing / /

DAY	LESSON 1 Details of Lesson	LESSON 2 Details of Lesson	LESSON 3 Details of Lesson	LESSON 4 Details of Lesson
MON				
TUES				
WED				
THURS				
FRI				

Events, Coaching, After School Sport Commitments etc for the week

LESSON 5 *Details of Lesson*	LESSON 6 *Details of Lesson*	LESSON 7 *Details of Lesson*	LESSON 8 *Details of Lesson*

SATURDAY	SUNDAY

Week Commencing / /

DAY	LESSON 1 Details of Lesson	LESSON 2 Details of Lesson	LESSON 3 Details of Lesson	LESSON 4 Details of Lesson
MON				
TUES				
WED				
THURS				
FRI				

Events, Coaching, After School Sport Commitments etc for the week

LESSON 5 Details of Lesson	LESSON 6 Details of Lesson	LESSON 7 Details of Lesson	LESSON 8 Details of Lesson

SATURDAY	SUNDAY

Week Commencing / /

DAY	LESSON 1 Details of Lesson	LESSON 2 Details of Lesson	LESSON 3 Details of Lesson	LESSON 4 Details of Lesson
MON				
TUES				
WED				
THURS				
FRI				

Events, Coaching, After School Sport Commitments etc for the week

LESSON 5 *Details of Lesson*	LESSON 6 *Details of Lesson*	LESSON 7 *Details of Lesson*	LESSON 8 *Details of Lesson*

SATURDAY	SUNDAY

Week Commencing / /

DAY	LESSON 1 *Details of Lesson*	LESSON 2 *Details of Lesson*	LESSON 3 *Details of Lesson*	LESSON 4 *Details of Lesson*
MON				
TUES				
WED				
THURS				
FRI				

Events, Coaching, After School Sport Commitments etc for the week

LESSON 5 *Details of Lesson*	LESSON 6 *Details of Lesson*	LESSON 7 *Details of Lesson*	LESSON 8 *Details of Lesson*

SATURDAY	SUNDAY

Week Commencing / /

DAY	LESSON 1 *Details of Lesson*	LESSON 2 *Details of Lesson*	LESSON 3 *Details of Lesson*	LESSON 4 *Details of Lesson*
MON				
TUES				
WED				
THURS				
FRI				

Events, Coaching, After School Sport Commitments etc for the week

LESSON 5 *Details of Lesson*	LESSON 6 *Details of Lesson*	LESSON 7 *Details of Lesson*	LESSON 8 *Details of Lesson*

SATURDAY	SUNDAY

Week Commencing / /

DAY	LESSON 1 *Details of Lesson*	LESSON 2 *Details of Lesson*	LESSON 3 *Details of Lesson*	LESSON 4 *Details of Lesson*
MON				
TUES				
WED				
THURS				
FRI				

Events, Coaching, After School Sport Commitments etc for the week

LESSON 5 *Details of Lesson*	LESSON 6 *Details of Lesson*	LESSON 7 *Details of Lesson*	LESSON 8 *Details of Lesson*

SATURDAY	SUNDAY

Week Commencing / /

DAY	LESSON 1 *Details of Lesson*	LESSON 2 *Details of Lesson*	LESSON 3 *Details of Lesson*	LESSON 4 *Details of Lesson*
MON				
TUES				
WED				
THURS				
FRI				

Events, Coaching, After School Sport Commitments etc for the week

LESSON 5 *Details of Lesson*	LESSON 6 *Details of Lesson*	LESSON 7 *Details of Lesson*	LESSON 8 *Details of Lesson*

SATURDAY	SUNDAY

Week Commencing / /

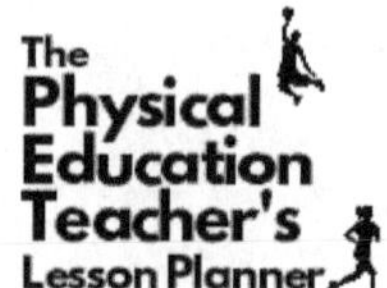

DAY	LESSON 1 Details of Lesson	LESSON 2 Details of Lesson	LESSON 3 Details of Lesson	LESSON 4 Details of Lesson
MON				
TUES				
WED				
THURS				
FRI				

Events, Coaching, After School Sport Commitments etc for the week

LESSON 5 *Details of Lesson*	LESSON 6 *Details of Lesson*	LESSON 7 *Details of Lesson*	LESSON 8 *Details of Lesson*

SATURDAY	SUNDAY

Week Commencing / /

DAY	LESSON 1 *Details of Lesson*	LESSON 2 *Details of Lesson*	LESSON 3 *Details of Lesson*	LESSON 4 *Details of Lesson*
MON				
TUES				
WED				
THURS				
FRI				

Events, Coaching, After School Sport Commitments etc for the week

LESSON 5 *Details of Lesson*	LESSON 6 *Details of Lesson*	LESSON 7 *Details of Lesson*	LESSON 8 *Details of Lesson*

SATURDAY	SUNDAY

Week Commencing   /   /

DAY	LESSON 1 *Details of Lesson*	LESSON 2 *Details of Lesson*	LESSON 3 *Details of Lesson*	LESSON 4 *Details of Lesson*
MON				
TUES				
WED				
THURS				
FRI				

Events, Coaching, After School Sport Commitments etc for the week

LESSON 5 *Details of Lesson*	LESSON 6 *Details of Lesson*	LESSON 7 *Details of Lesson*	LESSON 8 *Details of Lesson*

SATURDAY	SUNDAY

Week Commencing / /

DAY	LESSON 1 *Details of Lesson*	LESSON 2 *Details of Lesson*	LESSON 3 *Details of Lesson*	LESSON 4 *Details of Lesson*
MON				
TUES				
WED				
THURS				
FRI				

Events, Coaching, After School Sport Commitments etc for the week

LESSON 5 *Details of Lesson*	LESSON 6 *Details of Lesson*	LESSON 7 *Details of Lesson*	LESSON 8 *Details of Lesson*

SATURDAY	SUNDAY

Week Commencing / /

DAY	LESSON 1 Details of Lesson	LESSON 2 Details of Lesson	LESSON 3 Details of Lesson	LESSON 4 Details of Lesson
MON				
TUES				
WED				
THURS				
FRI				

Events, Coaching, After School Sport Commitments etc for the week

LESSON 5 *Details of Lesson*	LESSON 6 *Details of Lesson*	LESSON 7 *Details of Lesson*	LESSON 8 *Details of Lesson*

SATURDAY	SUNDAY

Week Commencing / /

DAY	LESSON 1 *Details of Lesson*	LESSON 2 *Details of Lesson*	LESSON 3 *Details of Lesson*	LESSON 4 *Details of Lesson*
MON				
TUES				
WED				
THURS				
FRI				

Events, Coaching, After School Sport Commitments etc for the week

LESSON 5 *Details of Lesson*	LESSON 6 *Details of Lesson*	LESSON 7 *Details of Lesson*	LESSON 8 *Details of Lesson*

SATURDAY	SUNDAY

Week Commencing / /

DAY	LESSON 1 Details of Lesson	LESSON 2 Details of Lesson	LESSON 3 Details of Lesson	LESSON 4 Details of Lesson
MON				
TUES				
WED				
THURS				
FRI				

Events, Coaching, After School Sport Commitments etc for the week

LESSON 5 *Details of Lesson*	LESSON 6 *Details of Lesson*	LESSON 7 *Details of Lesson*	LESSON 8 *Details of Lesson*

SATURDAY	SUNDAY

Week Commencing / /

DAY	LESSON 1 *Details of Lesson*	LESSON 2 *Details of Lesson*	LESSON 3 *Details of Lesson*	LESSON 4 *Details of Lesson*
MON				
TUES				
WED				
THURS				
FRI				

Events, Coaching, After School Sport Commitments etc for the week

LESSON 5 Details of Lesson	LESSON 6 Details of Lesson	LESSON 7 Details of Lesson	LESSON 8 Details of Lesson

SATURDAY	SUNDAY

Week Commencing / /

DAY	LESSON 1 *Details of Lesson*	LESSON 2 *Details of Lesson*	LESSON 3 *Details of Lesson*	LESSON 4 *Details of Lesson*
MON				
TUES				
WED				
THURS				
FRI				

Events, Coaching, After School Sport Commitments etc for the week

LESSON 5 *Details of Lesson*	LESSON 6 *Details of Lesson*	LESSON 7 *Details of Lesson*	LESSON 8 *Details of Lesson*

SATURDAY	SUNDAY

Week Commencing / /

DAY	LESSON 1 *Details of Lesson*	LESSON 2 *Details of Lesson*	LESSON 3 *Details of Lesson*	LESSON 4 *Details of Lesson*
MON				
TUES				
WED				
THURS				
FRI				

Events, Coaching, After School Sport Commitments etc for the week

LESSON 5 *Details of Lesson*	LESSON 6 *Details of Lesson*	LESSON 7 *Details of Lesson*	LESSON 8 *Details of Lesson*

SATURDAY	SUNDAY

Week Commencing / /

DAY	LESSON 1 *Details of Lesson*	LESSON 2 *Details of Lesson*	LESSON 3 *Details of Lesson*	LESSON 4 *Details of Lesson*
MON				
TUES				
WED				
THURS				
FRI				

Events, Coaching, After School Sport Commitments etc for the week

LESSON 5 Details of Lesson	LESSON 6 Details of Lesson	LESSON 7 Details of Lesson	LESSON 8 Details of Lesson

SATURDAY	SUNDAY

Week Commencing / /

DAY	LESSON 1 *Details of Lesson*	LESSON 2 *Details of Lesson*	LESSON 3 *Details of Lesson*	LESSON 4 *Details of Lesson*
MON				
TUES				
WED				
THURS				
FRI				

Events, Coaching, After School Sport Commitments etc for the week

LESSON 5 *Details of Lesson*	LESSON 6 *Details of Lesson*	LESSON 7 *Details of Lesson*	LESSON 8 *Details of Lesson*

SATURDAY	SUNDAY

Week Commencing / /

DAY	LESSON 1 Details of Lesson	LESSON 2 Details of Lesson	LESSON 3 Details of Lesson	LESSON 4 Details of Lesson
MON				
TUES				
WED				
THURS				
FRI				

Events, Coaching, After School Sport Commitments etc for the week

LESSON 5 *Details of Lesson*	**LESSON 6** *Details of Lesson*	**LESSON 7** *Details of Lesson*	**LESSON 8** *Details of Lesson*

SATURDAY	**SUNDAY**

Week Commencing / /

DAY	LESSON 1 Details of Lesson	LESSON 2 Details of Lesson	LESSON 3 Details of Lesson	LESSON 4 Details of Lesson
MON				
TUES				
WED				
THURS				
FRI				

Events, Coaching, After School Sport Commitments etc for the week

LESSON 5 *Details of Lesson*	LESSON 6 *Details of Lesson*	LESSON 7 *Details of Lesson*	LESSON 8 *Details of Lesson*

SATURDAY	SUNDAY

Week Commencing / /

DAY	LESSON 1 Details of Lesson	LESSON 2 Details of Lesson	LESSON 3 Details of Lesson	LESSON 4 Details of Lesson
MON				
TUES				
WED				
THURS				
FRI				

Events, Coaching, After School Sport Commitments etc for the week

LESSON 5 *Details of Lesson*	LESSON 6 *Details of Lesson*	LESSON 7 *Details of Lesson*	LESSON 8 *Details of Lesson*

SATURDAY	SUNDAY

Week Commencing / /

DAY	LESSON 1 *Details of Lesson*	LESSON 2 *Details of Lesson*	LESSON 3 *Details of Lesson*	LESSON 4 *Details of Lesson*
MON				
TUES				
WED				
THURS				
FRI				
Events, Coaching, After School Sport Commitments etc for the week				

LESSON 5 *Details of Lesson*	LESSON 6 *Details of Lesson*	LESSON 7 *Details of Lesson*	LESSON 8 *Details of Lesson*

SATURDAY	SUNDAY

Week Commencing / /

DAY	LESSON 1 *Details of Lesson*	LESSON 2 *Details of Lesson*	LESSON 3 *Details of Lesson*	LESSON 4 *Details of Lesson*
MON				
TUES				
WED				
THURS				
FRI				

Events, Coaching, After School Sport Commitments etc for the week

LESSON 5 *Details of Lesson*	LESSON 6 *Details of Lesson*	LESSON 7 *Details of Lesson*	LESSON 8 *Details of Lesson*

SATURDAY	SUNDAY

Week Commencing / /

DAY	LESSON 1 *Details of Lesson*	LESSON 2 *Details of Lesson*	LESSON 3 *Details of Lesson*	LESSON 4 *Details of Lesson*
MON				
TUES				
WED				
THURS				
FRI				
Events, Coaching, After School Sport Commitments etc for the week				

LESSON 5 *Details of Lesson*	LESSON 6 *Details of Lesson*	LESSON 7 *Details of Lesson*	LESSON 8 *Details of Lesson*

SATURDAY	SUNDAY

Week Commencing / /

DAY	LESSON 1 *Details of Lesson*	LESSON 2 *Details of Lesson*	LESSON 3 *Details of Lesson*	LESSON 4 *Details of Lesson*
MON				
TUES				
WED				
THURS				
FRI				

Events, Coaching, After School Sport Commitments etc for the week

LESSON 5 *Details of Lesson*	LESSON 6 *Details of Lesson*	LESSON 7 *Details of Lesson*	LESSON 8 *Details of Lesson*

SATURDAY	SUNDAY

Week Commencing / /

DAY	LESSON 1 Details of Lesson	LESSON 2 Details of Lesson	LESSON 3 Details of Lesson	LESSON 4 Details of Lesson
MON				
TUES				
WED				
THURS				
FRI				

Events, Coaching, After School Sport Commitments etc for the week

LESSON 5 *Details of Lesson*	LESSON 6 *Details of Lesson*	LESSON 7 *Details of Lesson*	LESSON 8 *Details of Lesson*

SATURDAY	SUNDAY

Week Commencing / /

DAY	LESSON 1 *Details of Lesson*	LESSON 2 *Details of Lesson*	LESSON 3 *Details of Lesson*	LESSON 4 *Details of Lesson*
MON				
TUES				
WED				
THURS				
FRI				

Events, Coaching, After School Sport Commitments etc for the week

LESSON 5 *Details of Lesson*	LESSON 6 *Details of Lesson*	LESSON 7 *Details of Lesson*	LESSON 8 *Details of Lesson*

SATURDAY	SUNDAY

Week Commencing / /

DAY	LESSON 1 Details of Lesson	LESSON 2 Details of Lesson	LESSON 3 Details of Lesson	LESSON 4 Details of Lesson
MON				
TUES				
WED				
THURS				
FRI				

Events, Coaching, After School Sport Commitments etc for the week

LESSON 5 *Details of Lesson*	LESSON 6 *Details of Lesson*	LESSON 7 *Details of Lesson*	LESSON 8 *Details of Lesson*

SATURDAY	SUNDAY

Week Commencing / /

DAY	LESSON 1 *Details of Lesson*	LESSON 2 *Details of Lesson*	LESSON 3 *Details of Lesson*	LESSON 4 *Details of Lesson*
MON				
TUES				
WED				
THURS				
FRI				

Events, Coaching, After School Sport Commitments etc for the week

LESSON 5 *Details of Lesson*	LESSON 6 *Details of Lesson*	LESSON 7 *Details of Lesson*	LESSON 8 *Details of Lesson*

SATURDAY	SUNDAY

Week Commencing / /

DAY	LESSON 1 *Details of Lesson*	LESSON 2 *Details of Lesson*	LESSON 3 *Details of Lesson*	LESSON 4 *Details of Lesson*
MON				
TUES				
WED				
THURS				
FRI				

Events, Coaching, After School Sport Commitments etc for the week

LESSON 5 *Details of Lesson*	LESSON 6 *Details of Lesson*	LESSON 7 *Details of Lesson*	LESSON 8 *Details of Lesson*

SATURDAY	SUNDAY

Physical Education - Game Play Fundermentals

Information provided courtesy of author Mark Dalton - 80 Awesome Sports Games

The Whistle

The effective use of the whistle, particularly in the outdoors is very important. The whistle in the majority of all circumstances should only be used to **STOP** an activity or movement. Students begin to get very confused if the whistle is used to start and stop activities and need to be informed of this from the very beginning. Fun whistle drills/activities can be used as a warm-up to teach this important rule. When blowing the whistle, it should be short & sharp and not 'fluffed'. Whistles can be a very commanding tool when used correctly.

Selecting Teams

One of the most frequent mistakes teachers often commit is the process of selecting teams. Many teachers have fallen for the trap of allowing their students to select teams with can have potentially negative outcomes.

Below are 3 reasons why students should not select their own teams.

1. It can isolate students that have social, learning and/or physical difficulties
2. Can damage self-esteem of students selected last
3. Can result in teams comprising of students with behavior personalities that may clash

It is therefore important for teachers to select teams due to the following reasons.
- Teachers will select a variety of ability levels to ensure teams are even.
- Teachers can select quickly and efficiently to avoid wasted lesson time
- Less confrontation will occur if the teacher's decision is final on team selection

Physical Education - Game Play Fundermentals

Information provided courtesy of author Mark Dalton - 80 Awesome Sports Games

Basic Safety Guidelines

The initial priority for a teacher is the safety of the participants. The teacher will need to consider the participant numbers, indoor or outdoor space, age level of the students and equipment required for the game. These will dictate the safety measures required to run the game in a safe environment and to avoid any potential hazards. The teacher may wish to ask the students to name potential safety hazards in the playing area. This encourages the students to visually identify possible dangers, therefore giving the teacher the opportunity to educate the students on dangers around them and promote safe play.

Teachers should attempt to follow the equipment guidelines as set out in the book as closely as possible. Modifying the equipment may be necessary according to the resources available to the teacher although consideration must be taken if equipment will be used in confined spaces or will be making contact with the participants.

Other considerations needed for the safety of participants is the effective use of the whistle to stop activities and the environmental conditions if participating outdoors.

Positioning – Outdoor Activities

The majority of teachers with little or next to no experience have difficulties controlling activities outdoors. It is most important that students are addressed within close proximity of the teacher due to the following reasons:

1. Windy Conditions can stifle the ability to communicate clearly and effectively to your students. Attempt to find a protected area away from the wind. If possible, have your students sit or kneel and in a tight group. Project your voice and ensure you make eye contact when giving instructions to avoid speaking towards the ground. Unless you have a powerful voice and experience in teaching outdoors, avoid giving instructions in lessons when the class is well spread.

2. Bright Sunshine and moving objects in the background can be a huge distraction to any year level. The teacher should position themselves so they are looking into the sun and/or ensuring the group have their back turned to the distraction.

Physical Education - Game Play Fundermentals

Information provided courtesy of author Mark Dalton - 80 Awesome Sports Games

Encouraging good behavior, sportsmanship & participation

Playing a variety of games with your students is a terrific way to encourage and enforce good behavior, sportsmanship and participation. There will be many opportunities to promote and make an example of good behavior. Rewarding teams with 'bonus' points/runs for teamwork or sportsmanship will encourage others to do likewise. "Nick, I'm very impressed with the way you contributed with setting up the field without even being asked. Your team will receive 5 bonus points to your final score".

Avoid taking points away from teams own score for poor behavior as this may have a negative impact on the rest of the team members if they are behaving appropriately. Penalizing a team for one individual's poor sportsmanship or behavior could potentially cause problems.

The teacher could respond in the following ways

1. Add a point to the oppositions score (rather than remove a point from their own score)
2. Provide a clear warning to the student/s that any further poor behavior will not be tolerated and they will have a 5 – 10 minute timeout.
3. The student must remain behind to collect and pack away the game equipment

It is always important to involve all students in the running of the game. Students with an injury or illness could assist with the scoring, time-keeping, distribution of colour tags etc (at teacher's discretion). Participation will increase if the teacher is enthusiastic about the game, becomes involved with the activity, praises good sportsmanship and acknowledges teamwork.

Equipment set-up and pack-down should also be incorporated into the time available for the lesson.

Getting Involved and Having Fun

Students will enjoy the games you play much more if you become involved. There are many ways the teacher can participate actively in a game.

1. The 'neutral' bowler for each team. This is beneficial for younger age groups so the ball can be rolled at an even pace and can be adapted to different skill levels in the batting team.
2. Spare fieldsman for both teams. The teacher can then be on hand to stop the game for teachable moments or to enforce rule violations.
3. The teacher can be the official scorer or you can delegate to children with an illness or injury if possible. In many instances the designated umpire/referee for games should be the teacher for younger age levels but this can be adjusted for older age groups to encourage students to gain officiating experience.

Physical Education - Game Play Fundermentals

Information provided courtesy of author Mark Dalton - 80 Awesome Sports Games

Handling Violations

Like any form of game involving rules and regulations, teachers should ensure the participants are aware of these prior to a game commencing. If the teacher is instructing younger children, games can be paused (teachable moment) and the teacher can explain the rules as they occur. Younger children find it difficult to process rules without visually seeing how the game is played and by getting the children involved will enable them to have a much better understanding of the rules & regulations as the game is played.

Being strict on the rules from the very beginning is important as it will set the tone for the remainder of the game. Poor behavior is likely if students are not clear on the rules of the game, if some rules are not enforced at the commencement of the activity and if the game is not suited to the age level of the students. Teachers need to remain vigilant on any rule violations and ensure the student/s is clear as to why the infringement was made. Students will continue to make similar mistakes if violations are not explained to them in the first instance by the teacher.

Additional Game Advice

Encourage students to share the ball among all team members. Acknowledge this with bonus points or team rewards

1. Avoid disciplining a student with a physical activity. E.g. "Tom, stop misbehaving. You can now run 4 laps of the field". Exercising should be a positive, not a negative experience for students.
2. Always conclude 5 minutes early. This provides the opportunity for all students to contribute in the collection of equipment. It can also be a good opportunity to reflect on the skills performed during the lessons and areas of improvement for next time.
3. When learning new skills, select children that can demonstrate to the rest of the class. These opportunities can be a great way to build self-esteem for the student but also encourage other students to be selected to also demonstrate new skills.
4. Avoid games for younger children with lengthy periods of time on the sidelines or waiting their turn to bat etc. Students will often become restless and this often leads to misbehavior.

notes.

notes.

notes.

CPSIA information can be obtained
at www.ICGtesting.com
Printed in the USA
LVHW051021040820
662292LV00015B/325